Graham's Golf Club

Alex Graham is a Scot from Dumfries educated at Dumfries Academy and Glasgow School of Art. He has been a full-time cartoonist since 1945 and worked for all the leading British magazines and had a series in the *New Yorker*. At one time he did three weekly strips in addition to Fred Basset in the *Daily Mail* but now concentrates principally on that strip, which was started in 1963 and is now syndicated world-wide and has been made into twenty TV short films.

Alex Graham lives in Sussex beside a lake, plays golf and bridge, gardens, and has two dogs. He married a fellow student and has a grown-up son and daughter.

With love to Winifred,
my wife,
and favourite foursomes partner

Also, thanks to my fellow members of Rye Golf Club,
Sussex, who supplied (unwittingly)
many of the ideas

Alex Graham

of *The Sunday Telegraph*

Graham's Golf Club

A Pan Original

Pan Books

London, Sydney and Auckland

First published 1990 by Pan Books Ltd
Cavaye Place, London SW10 9PG
in association with *The Sunday Telegraph*

9 8 7 6 5 4 3 2 1

ISBN 0 330 31658 3

Photoset by Parker Typesetting Service, Leicester
Printed in England by Clays Ltd, St Ives plc

"I've just shanked my way round the course with this seven iron you sold me!"

"Just enough breeze to test those youngsters."

"Now isn't this better than tramping round
the golf course?"

"I'm beginning to suspect that there may be more to this game than I thought."

"Perimeter weighted heads? . . . Velocitised steel shafts?
Offset hosels? Low kick point?"

"Could you go over that bit again about a strong grip helping to control the power generated in the swing by centrifugal force?"

"I shanked my way through '90,
but I hope for better things in '91."

"That's what my husband always says when he misses a short putt."

"Great shot, old man! . . . Well played!"

"I always think the course is at its most beautiful when it dons its autumnal carpet of russet leaves."

GRAHAM

"Did you see an electric trolley go past?"

"Grown men gallivanting about in that thing!"

"I BEAT HIM!"

"Mummy, what's the Open Championship?"

"I don't believe in fancy theories.
One or two waggles, then I whack it!"

"Seven days in the Algarve? . . . Love to!
Count me in. Of course I can get away."

QUIET
RYDER CUP
ALEX GRAHAM

"It's all that beer they drank at lunchtime!"

"I'm surprised you're not losing patience with me."

"Before we start, Maureen, I would like to say
that that is a really lovely skirt."

"He'll never reach it with a seven iron."

"It bounced on to the green, and he sank the putt for an eagle."

"If it's a boy we could call him Severiano."

"... resulting in a sizeable deficit. Which brings me to the question of the annual subscription ..."

"I can't, Rodney, I can't. It's resting on a primrose!"

"I've walked my dogs over those fields for twenty years, young man, and I shall continue to do so!"

"Doesn't ANYONE want a few holes before lunch?"

"When I want your advice, sonny, I'll ask for it."

"We had a really great game, and I won seven and six."

"CANCELLED? My lesson?"

"Well, that's '91 off to a flying start."

"Anybody get his number?"

"I always think Rye is at its best in January!"

"Mummy! . . . Daddy's won a cup!"

"Heel, Sevvy! . . . Down, Woosey! . . . Keep up, Sandy!"

"Bad news, Sir! You're suffering from an incurable slice!"

"He'll grow into it."

"Sorry, Sir! I don't stock hickory-shafted cleeks."

"I keep losing the damn things!"

"We'll have to play a three ball."

"Give it up, Angus! You'll never find a green tee-peg in that lot!"

"Come home, Mervyn, and the hell with tomorrow's Monthly Medal!"

"If you kept your head still, Miss Partridge, your hairpins wouldn't fall out!"

"You've hit that Ford Sierra again!"

"Sand wedge."

"I could possibly fit you in for nine holes around the end of October."

"Yes, your husband is still here, madam. . . .
Lunch is ruined. . . . I'll tell him, madam."

"Having her hair permed? . . . On Medal Day!"

"Happy New Year!"

"Well, approximately then."

". . . I hit a goodish drive – not long but nice and straight – then took a four iron and . . ."

"I overclubbed."

"They're going to increase the subscription in '91."

"I'm five up!"

"If we'd known, we could have gone to church!"

"Next on the agenda, the clubhouse roof."

"Trying a new grip . . . dislocated his thumb."

"Four wood!"

ALEX
GRAHAM
SWINGRITE

Links
View
ALEX
GRAHAM

"Par four, isn't it?"

"Time I was off. I've left Buster tied up outside."

“Fiona . . . Hold lunch!
We’re stuck behind an elderly four ball!”

"Nick Faldo's just had another birdie!"

"Where can I get hold of a membership application form?"

"Isn't he awful? Sorry about the teeth marks."

"Do draw up a chair and tell me all about this marvellous round of yours."

"Madam, is that or is that not a rabbit scrape?"

"Why can't you be laid back and relaxed
like Sandy Lyle?"

"I think I'm getting the hang of it."

"Put it off? Because of a little shower?"

"Arthur, PLEASE declare it unplayable and come down!"

"Approximately when did you first feel the yips coming on?"

"Another lesson or two, and the course record will be at your mercy."

"This is nothing! You should see him on one of his good days."

"Think positively partner! Ask yourself how Sandy Lyle would tackle this little problem."

"FORE! . . . I mean FIRE!"

"Hold it chaps! Booking error! Not expected till tomorrow!"

"Four up and five to play
and he beat me on the eighteenth!"

"I'm doing my best, partner!"

"Same time next Saturday, lads."

"What on earth's that you've got there?"

"Every golf club has its eccentric."

"Young whippersnapper!"

"Then take it off the heat and just before it sets fold in the double cream . . ."

"... and look forward with pride to my year as Captain of this great Golf Club. In conclusion ..."

"I don't know about you, Moira, but I'd give anything for a cup of tea."

"There, there, Mrs Gibson! You mustn't lose heart!"

"And who owns the wet spaniel in the drying room?"

"Now partner, I want you to rifle a four iron over the oak tree, with a touch of fade to clear the pond, skirt the bunker, and drift on to the green."

"It's at this point I get the searing pain through my left ankle."

"I've often wondered if Señora Ballesteros has to put up with this sort of thing."

"Get rid of the garage, and I could fit in another nine holes."

"Pack it in? . . . And me three up!"

"Daddy knows perfectly well that it's made of metal, Timmy, but nevertheless it's a four wood."

NO SMOKING
REPLACE DIVOTS
RAKE BUNKERS
NO DOGS
1st TEE
GIVE WAY TO FASTER PLAYERS
ALEX GRAHAM

"That's new!"

"Please can Dudley come out to play?"

"Did either of you young people
see a golf ball arrive?"

"I shouldn't find it difficult –
at school I was a jolly good hockey player."

"Are you quite sure I only need a little flick with a sand iron?"

"There may be golf on television," I said,
"but I'm not putting off my bridge four."

"You know the rules, sir!
The clubhouse closes at nine o'clock."

"In the event of the committee approving your application, your name will then go onto the waiting list."

"We can't go on meeting like this, Penny."

"Take your partners for a mixed foursome . . . Sorry! I mean a slow foxtrot."

"It looks quite a nice game,
but I doubt if it will catch on."